Edition Schott

Clarinet Library · Klarinetten-Bibliothek

Carl Maria von Weber

1786 – 1826

Grand Duo concertant

for Clarinet (in B♭) and Piano
für Klarinette (in B) und Klavier

opus 48 (JV 204, WeV P. 12)

Nach dem Text der Carl-Maria-von Weber-Gesamtausgabe herausgegeben von
Edited from Carl Maria von Weber, Complete Works by
Knut Holtsträter

KLB 58
ISMN 979-0-001-14095-9

www.schott-music.com

Mainz · London · Berlin · Madrid · New York · Paris · Prag · Tokyo · Toronto
© 2005 SCHOTT MUSIC GmbH & Co. KG, Mainz · Printed in Germany

Vorwort

Praktische Ausgaben auf der Basis von kritischen belasten den Herausgeber stets mit einem schlechten Gewissen: Zum einen suggeriert der vorliegende Notentext eine Genauigkeit, die oftmals schon durch die verschiedenen Quellen nicht gegeben ist. Zum anderen bieten sie eine ‚entschlackte' Version, frei vom Ballast der Lesartenverzeichnisse, die die Entscheidungen des Herausgebers jedoch erst rechtfertigen bzw. sie ggf. auch relativieren. Für ein genaueres Studium der Sachverhalte sei daher das entsprechende Kapitel in Serie VI, Band 3 der Weber-Gesamtausgabe nachdrücklich empfohlen.

Zur Entstehung des Werkes

Weber hat das *Grand Duo* in enger Zusammenarbeit mit seinem Freund, dem Klarinettisten Heinrich Joseph Baermann, komponiert. Wie bei vielen anderes Werken Webers entstanden die Sätze in der umgekehrten Reihenfolge, d. h. zuerst das *Rondo*, welches er laut Tagebuch am 8. Juli 1815 mit Baermann einübte. Am Abend des 11. Juli folgte die Skizzierung des II. Satzes. Die erste verbürgte Aufführung des *Rondo*-Satzes durch Weber und Baermann fand am 18. Juli 1815 im privaten Rahmen statt, die erste Aufführung beider Sätze folgte am 2. August im Münchner Hoftheater. Die Skizzierung und Fertigstellung des Kopfsatzes ließ etwa eineinhalb Jahre auf sich warten. Weber vermerkte am 5. November 1816 im Tagebuch: „gearbeitet. *Duo* in *Es*. ersten Theil notiert.", und bereits am 8. November heißt es „*Allo*. in *Es* zum *Clar. Pf: Duo* vollendet". Etwa ein halbes Jahr später wurde das Werk vom Verlag Schlesinger publiziert.

Zu den Quellen des Werkes

Es ist ein vermutlich Anfang November 1816 in Berlin entstandenes autographes Fragment der T. 59-129 des I. Satzes in der Staatsbibliothek zu Berlin – Preußischer Kulturbesitz (Signatur: Mus. ms. autogr. C. M. v. Weber 4) erhalten, das aufgrund seiner Beschaffenheit als Teil eines vermutlich kompletten Entwurfs dieses Satzes zu werten ist, der im Herbst 1816 in Berlin entstand. Weber hat in diesem Entwurf bereits zahlreiche Angaben zur Dynamik, Artikulation, Phrasierung und Ausführung eingetragen, die er allerdings z. T. nicht in seine autographe Reinschrift übernahm. Das Fragment spielte für die Erstellung des vorliegenden Notentextes keine Rolle, enthält aber als Vorstufe der Reinschrift einige interessante Varianten, die Einblicke in Webers Arbeitsweise geben (vgl. WeGA VI/3, S. 179-181).

Folgende Quellen sind für die Konstitution des Notentextes herangezogen worden:

1. Die autographe Reinschrift:
Washington, Library of Congress, Signatur: ML30.8b.W4 Op. 48

Das für Webers Handarchiv erstellte Autograph ist am Ende des *Rondo* mit „München d: 6t *July* 1815" datiert, kann aber frühestens im November 1816 in Berlin(?) fertiggestellt worden sein.
Die wenigen vorhandenen Korrekturen in dem sehr dicht und platzsparend geschriebenen Autograph sind vermutlich im Schreibvorgang ausgeführt worden. Die Bezeichnung mit dynamischen und artikulatorischen Zeichen ist äußerst sparsam und entspricht dem Verfahren in Webers übrigen Archivexemplaren. Eigenartigerweise ist in den Sätzen II und III die Angabe „*Cembalo*", abweichend davon aber im I. Satz die Angabe „*Pianoforte*" zu finden. Für die Edition hat die Handschrift aufgrund ihres Archivcharakters lediglich die Bedeutung einer Vergleichsquelle, die in Einzelfällen zudem Auszeichnungs-Varianten überliefert.

2. Die Stichvorlage:
Wien, Stadt- und Landesbibliothek, Musiksammlung, Signatur: MH 14423/c.

Es handelt sich um eine Kopistenabschrift mit zahlreichen autographen Nachträgen, die vermutlich Ende 1816 in Berlin als Stichvorlage für Schlesinger angefertigt wurde. Sie ist sehr sauber und in gleichmäßiger Seiten- und Takteinteilung beschrieben. Als Quelle lag dabei offensichtlich die autographe Reinschrift Webers zugrunde, denn der Kopist übernahm nicht nur die unterschiedlichen Besetzungsangaben und Satz- bzw. Tempobezeichnungen wörtlich, sondern folgte auch ansonsten mit graphischer Genauigkeit der Vorlage. Weber hat diese Abschrift sehr gründlich durchgesehen und zahllose Details der Dynamik, Agogik, Artikulation und Phrasierung ergänzt, während er – wie auch bei anderen Werken – die Richtigkeit der Töne offensichtlich kaum kontrollierte. Im direkten Vergleich der Quellen zeigt sich, dass Weber die Kopie wohl ohne Rückgriff auf sein Autograph bezeichnete, da in etlichen Einzelheiten unterschiedliche Bezeichnungsweisen festzustellen sind. Als unmittelbar für die Anfertigung des Drucks gedachte Vorlage enthält diese Handschrift das Werk in seiner definitiven Form. Da zweifelhaft bleibt, ob Weber Druckfahnen korrigiert hat, und andererseits der Stecher im Erstdruck einige Details des Manuskripts ungenau wiedergibt bzw. missverstanden hat, stellt nicht der Erstdruck, sondern diese Stichvorlage die Hauptquelle für die Edition des Werkes dar.

3. Der Erstdruck bei Schlesinger:
Berlin: Adolph Martin Schlesinger, Plattennummer „253" (1817); ohne Opuszahl auf dem Titelblatt

Im Vergleich mit der Stichvorlage findet sich im Erstdruck zwar eine verhältnismäßig geringe Zahl von Übertragungsfehlern, allerdings wurden etliche Angaben zur Dynamik oder Artikulation aus der Stichvorlage nicht übernommen. Wie in vielen Schlesinger-Drucke dieser Zeit wurden Webers staccato-Striche nahezu durchgängig als Punkte übertragen. Nicht auf Missverständnisse oder freie Interpretation zurückgehende Änderungen bzw. eigene Zutaten des Stechers sind dagegen äußerst selten.

Zur Druckgeschichte des Werkes und zur Baermann-Ausgabe

Wie bei fast allen Kammermusikwerken Webers muss man auch beim *Grand Duo*, das bald zum Standardrepertoire der Klarinettisten gehörte, eine recht verworrene Druckgeschichte konstatieren. Eine Hauptlinie der Überlieferung bilden dabei die Drucke, die im Hause von Webers Berliner Hauptverleger Adolph Martin Schlesinger, seines in Paris wirkenden Sohnes Moritz und der Nachfolger Schlesingers (Lienau) hergestellt wurden. Von Interesse ist vor allem die Überlieferung bis hin zu den im gleichen Hause erschienenen Ausgaben von Heinrich Baermanns Sohn Carl Baermann. (Diese verschiedenen Überlieferungswege und die einzelnen Drucke sind in Bd. VI/3, der WeGA, S. 150-164, ausführlich beschrieben und anhand einiger besonders markanter, hartnäckiger „Glättungen" bzw. Fehler analysiert worden.)

Im Zuge seiner Neueditionen der weberschen Klarinettenwerke für Schlesingers *Gesammtausgabe* bearbeitete Carl Baermann Ende 1869 auch das *Grand Duo*, wobei er die Klavierstimme des ihm vorliegenden postumen Schlesinger-Drucks sorgfältig durchgesehen, verbliebene Fehler beseitigt und teilweise durch seine Notationsweise den Notentext verdeutlicht sowie die Solostimme detailliert bezeichnet hat. Während er sich in diesem Falle aller Eingriffe in Tonhöhen und -dauern enthalten hat, ist die Ausgabe wiederum übersät mit Angaben zur Artikulation, Phrasierung und Dynamik. Dabei sind insbesondere zahlreiche Akzente und meist ein- oder zweitaktige *crescendo-decrescendo*-Verläufe ergänzt worden. Gelegentlich sind *legato*-Bögen in *staccato*-Bezeichnungen umgewandelt (z. B. im I. Satz in T. 47ff. oder im III. Satz bei Sechzehntelfiguren der Klarinette, etwa in T. 13/14) oder auch staccato-Passagen durch Einfügung kleinräumiger Bögen unterbrochen worden.

Den von Weber bis zum Ende des III. Satzes (T. 236ff.) aufgesparten Effekt der gegen die Taktschwerpunkte gesetzten Akzente etwa hat Baermann bereits beim ersten Auftreten des *grazioso*-Gedankens (vgl. T. 68ff.) angebracht. Zu Beginn des langsamen Satzes ist in T. 5 der Klarinette „con duolo" durch „con tutt'anima" ersetzt, statt des *decrescendo* in T. 63 ist zunächst ein *crescendo* angegeben. Auch das „ritard." in T. 141 des I. Satzes ist eine Zutat. Im III. Satz versuchte Baermann die in Webers Notierung unklare Fortsetzung des Trillers der Klarinette in T. 196f. und 200f. durch eine eingeschobene Achtel-Vorschlagsnote *h* vor T. 197 bzw. T. 201 zu präzisieren.

Trotz dieser dem überlieferten Notentext widersprechenden Festlegungen der Artikulation und Dynamik bis in kleinste Details ist der Grad der Eingriffe Baermanns hier im Vergleich zu den übrigen Klarinettenwerken gering. Seine Edition wurde dann aber für neuerliche Arrangements und spätere Ausgaben des Werkes stets mit herangezogen, so dass sie direkt oder indirekt unsere gesamte Rezeption des *Grand Duo* beeinflusste. Die vorliegende Ausgabe kehrt zum dem Zustand des Werkes „vor Baermann" zurück. Der mit der Baermann-Ausgabe vertraute Musiker wird feststellen, dass die originalen Phrasierungsbögen weiter und die Bezeichnungen der Artikulation homogener sind, so dass die ‚Kurzatmigkeit', die das Werk im Laufe seiner Rezeption befallen hat, aufgehoben wird. Betont sei, dass Weber gerade der Gestaltungsbereich des ‚akzidentellen Notentextes' durchaus wichtig war – die fein ausgearbeiteten Varianten der Artikulation des Rondothemas (T. 68ff. und 236ff.) sind ein Indiz dafür.

Zur vorliegenden Edition und zu einigen Notationsbesonderheiten Webers

Die Notation der Neuausgabe folgt soweit möglich den jeweiligen Hauptquellen nach den Prinzipien der WeGA. Ergänzungen in Übereinstimmung mit anderen Quellen erscheinen in runden, Zusätze des Herausgebers in eckigen Klammern.

Es ist zu bedenken, dass nicht bezeichnete Stellen selten wörtlich zu nehmen sind bzw. eine vorherige **Artikulation** nicht automatisch außer Kraft setzen. Vielmehr können solche Takte teilweise in Anlehnung an Paralleltakte interpretiert oder im Sinne der bei Weber häufig zu beobachtenden Tendenz zu Varianten bezeichnet werden. So liegen z. B. in Satz I die Übertragung der *staccati* auf die rH in T. 139 und T. 161 analog der vorangehenden Parallelstelle sehr nahe. Die vom Kopisten in der Stichvorlage bzw. von Weber häufig verwendeten Ton- oder Akkordrepetitions-Kürzel wurden in der Regel beibehalten, aber aufgelöst, wenn dadurch Verunsicherungen auftreten könnten.

Die rhythmische Bezeichnung von **Vor- und Nachschlägen** zu einzelnen Noten oder Trillern weicht zwischen den Quellen, aber oft auch innerhalb einer Handschriften ab. Weber bevorzugt bei Vorschlägen aus Einzelnoten die Form ♪, bei zwei oder mehr Tönen unabhängig vom Metrum die Wiedergabe in 32teln. Für **Appoggiaturen** verwendet er neben der Form ♪ auch gewöhnliche kleiner notierte Achtelwerte. Der Kopist übernahm die Vorschläge meist von Weber.

Die eigentümlichen **Bogenführungen** wurden als Charakteristikum Webers bewahrt, sie führen aber stellenweise zu einer „sperrig" wirkenden Wiedergabe des Notentextes, die die Interpretation des Lesenden herausfordert. Durch Webers unpräzise und uneinheitliche Bogensetzung lässt sich beim *Rondo*-Thema des III. Satzes nicht bestimmen, inwieweit die vielfältigen Abweichungen Absicht sind oder zumindest teilweise auf Nachlässigkeiten in der Notierung oder gar auf der Unterscheidung von **Artikulations- und Phrasierungsbögen** beruhen. Auch beim Aufgreifen der Bassfigur im Mittelteil T. 136ff. ist schwer entscheidbar, ob eine Differenzierung beabsichtigt ist. Der Herausgeber hat daher hier die Bögen mit der für ihn erkennbaren Präzision der Vorlage wiedergegeben und lediglich einige behutsame (gekennzeichnete) Korrekturen eingefügt. Durchgängig verwendet Weber zur Bezeichnung eines *sempre-legato-* oder *sempre-portato*-Spiels in wiederholten bzw. durchlaufenden Begleitfiguren mehrtaktige Phrasierungsbögen, die teils willkürlich mit ein- oder mehrtaktigen (oft auch überlappenden bzw. aneinander anschließenden) Bögen wechseln. In solchen Fällen dürfen die Bögen nicht als Neubeginn eines Artikulationsabschnitts missverstanden werden. Diese Annahme wird gestützt durch die hier oft zu beobachtenden Notationsunterschiede der verschiedenen Quellen (vgl. z.B. im Klaviersatz T. 64ff., 88ff., 126ff., 259ff. im I. Satz, T. 9ff. u. 71ff. im II. und T. 163ff. im III. Satz). Zusätzliche Probleme ergeben sich bei alberti-artigen Begleitfiguren (z.B. Satz I, T. 259ff.), wo die die unterschiedlich langen, aneinander anschließenden Bögen der rH lediglich ein *legato*-Spiel fordern, so wie zu Beginn von Satz II, T. 5 bzw. 8ff. die unpräzise gesetzten Bögen ein *portato*. Besonders Pausen-überspannende oder offen endende Bögen bei repetierenden Figuren (wie im III. Satz, T. 61–62 rH oder T. 147–150 unteres System) belegen, dass diese Bögen lediglich Spielanweisung sind und keine Gliederung anzeigen sollen.

Die in ihrer Bedeutung bisher nicht eindeutig geklärte Unterscheidung von **Strich und Punkt** lässt sich bei Weber auch im *Grand Duo* beobachten und wurde vom Herausgeber – soweit unterscheidbar – beibehalten.

Der Kopist der Stichvorlage hat die Striche Webers zu Punkten vereinheitlicht; die dort zugesetzten Striche sind Nachträge Webers, die dann im Druck wiederum größtenteils in Punkte umgesetzt wurden. Als ein Charakteristikum kann auch die Verwendung des Strichs am Ende eines Bogens bezeichnet werden. Offensichtlich ist hiermit generell eine Kürzung des Notenwerts intendiert. Ähnliches gilt für die Striche zu Anfang oder in der Mitte des Bogens, z.B. in Satz I, T. 253–254, linke Hand.

Innerhalb der teils sehr unvollständigen und oft kaum eindeutig zu ergänzenden Angaben Webers zur **Dynamik** bleiben u. a. etliche **Akzent-Zeichen** unklar, da durch ihre Größe von *decrescendo-Gabeln* kaum unterscheidbar. Selbst unmittelbar aufeinanderfolgende, motivisch gleiche Stellen können unterschiedlich bezeichnet sein, wie etwa die Klarinette im III. Satz (dort in der Stichvorlage, T. 212, Länge einer *decrescendo*-Gabel und T. 214 gewöhnliches Akzentzeichen, beides Zusätze Webers). In solchen Fällen kann der Herausgeber im edierten Text nur jeweils seine Lesart wiedergeben.

Erwähnenswert ist in diesem Zusammenhang eine Korrektur Webers im III. Satz, wo der Kopist in T. 17 den Akzent zur langen Note der Klarinette übernommen hatte, Weber ihn aber durch *fp* überschreibt. Beide Bezeichnungsweisen scheinen also nicht synonym. Obwohl Weber vermutlich – wie die Eintragung im Autograph zeigt – aus Gründen der Schreibökonomie die „einfachere" Notierungsform bevorzugt, scheint das Akzentzeichen also grundsätzlich in zwei Formen deutbar, so dass besonders bei langen Notenwerten stets eine mögliche Differenzierung zu bedenken ist. (Einen Hinweis die Bedeutungsunterschiede gibt auch eine Änderung in T. 59, wo Weber den vom Kopisten wiederum aus dem Autograph übernommenen Akzent der Klarinette durch eine längere, über die gesamte Dauer des Notenwertes reichende *decrescendo*-Gabel überschrieben hat. Zugleich aber ersetzt er den Akzent der linken Hand durch ein *fp*).

Webers **Klavierschreibweise** weicht insofern von der heute üblichen Notierungsform ab als er vielfach beide Systeme zur Darstellung des musikalischen Verlaufs bzw. der Stimmführung nutzt. Die häufige Notation beider Hände in einem System (z. B. Satz I, T. 126ff.) oder das Fortsetzen begonnener Figuren im je anderen (z. B. Satz I, T. 166ff. oder 198ff.) dienen also der besseren Übersicht über musikalische Verläufe und wurden vom Hg. beibehalten. Pedalanweisungen hat Weber nur im II. Satz zu den *portati* in T. 37ff. und T. 51 sowie im III. Satz, T. 217, eingetragen.

Während in den beiden letzten Fällen die akkordische Ausfüllung eines G-Dur-Klangs bzw. die Repetitionen eines B-Dur-Septakkords als Klangfläche durch die Aufhebung der Dämpfung gestützt wird, soll im ersten Beispiel offensichtlich die hohe Lage der rH in ähnlicher Weise klanglich hervorgehoben werden. (Webers Brodmann-Flügel hatte außer dem Dämpfungspedal noch ein *una-corda*-Pedal, einen Fagottzug sowie ein *piano*-Pedal, hier dürfte aber nur die Aufhebung der Dämpfung bezeichnet sein.) Der Pedalwechsel ist hier vermutlich durch die Bögen mit bezeichnet.

Die Auflösung der Kürzel zur Bezeichnung der 32tel-**Tremoli** im Finalsatz T. 125ff. ist in unterschiedlicher Weise möglich, wie dies auch die verschiedenen Editionen des Werkes belegen.

Die Notation **alternativer Töne** für die erste Takthälfte von T. 196 der Klarinette in Satz I hängt möglicherweise mit instrumententechnischen Gegebenheiten zusammen, wobei offensichtlich nicht die Einzeltöne, sondern die Folge der drei ersten Töne als Problem gelten muss. Die Notationsweise der Klarinette im Anfangsteil der Durchführung des I. Satzes (T. 130bff.) wurde trotz der eigentlich inkorrekten Bezeichnungsweise um der besseren Lesbarkeit willen beibehalten.

Allen, die zur Entstehung dieser Edition beigetragen haben, sei an dieser Stelle ein herzlicher Dank gesagt.

Knut Holtsträter

Preface

Practical editions that are based on critical editions always burden the editor with pangs of conscience: on the one hand, the score in front of us suggests a precision which is often not provided by the various sources. On the other hand, this offers a 'purified' version free of the ballast of references used to justify or explain the editor's decisions. For closer examination of the details involved, it is urged that reference be made to the corresponding chapter in Series VI, vol. 3 of the Weber *Gesamtausgabe*, the complete edition of his works.

Genesis of the work

Weber composed the *Grand Duo* in close collaboration with his friend the clarinettist Heinrich Joseph Baermann. As with many of Weber's other works, the movements were written in reverse order, i.e. beginning with the *Rondo*, which he rehearsed with Baermann on 8 July 1815, according to his diary. On the evening of 11 July the second movement was sketched out. The first documented performance of the *Rondo* movement by Weber and Baermann was given in a private house on 18 July 1815 and the first performance of both movements together followed on 2 August in the Munich *Hoftheater*. The sketching out and completion of the first movement was not done until late in the following year. On 5 November 1816

Weber wrote in his diary: "Worked. Notated first part of *Duo* in *E flat*." and by the 8 November the diary entry states that he had already "finished *Allo*. in *E flat* for *Clar. Pf. Duo*". The work was published by Schlesinger about six months later.

The sources for the work

An autograph fragment of bars 59-129 of the first movement, probably written in Berlin at the beginning of November 1816, is kept in the *Staatsbibliothek zu Berlin – Preußischer Kulturbesitz* (shelf mark: Mus. ms. autogr. C. M. v. Weber 4); this needs to be evaluated as part of what was presumably a complete draft version of this movement composed in Berlin in the autumn of 1816. In this draft version Weber includes numerous indications regarding dynamics, articulation, phrasing and performance, though some of these were not carried over into his own autograph fair copy. This fragment was not used a basis for the present score, though as a preliminary to the fair copy this source contains some interesting variants which give an insight into Weber's working methods (see WeGA VI/3, pp. 179-181).

The following source documents were used as the basis for this score:

1. The autograph fair copy
Washington, Library of Congress, shelf mark: ML30.8b.W4 Op. 48

This autograph score was written out for Weber's own reference archive and is dated at the end of the *Rondo* "Munich 6 *July* 1815", but at the earliest it cannot have been completed until November 1816 in Berlin(?).
The few corrections that appear in the very densely written autograph score were probably made in the process of writing the score, as very little space is left. As in the other scores that Weber wrote out for his archive, there are very few indications of dynamics and articulation. Strangely enough, in movements II and III a *"Cembalo" [harpsichord]* is specified, while in movement I a different specification of *"Pianoforte"* appears. In view of its archival character, the manuscript can serve only as a comparative source for the present edition; it also provides variant markings in a number of places.

2. The engraver's proof
Vienna, Stadt- und Landesbibliothek, music collection, shelf mark: MH 14423/c.

This is a copyist's copy with numerous additions by the composer, probably prepared for Schlesinger as an engraver's copy-text in Berlin at the end of 1816. It is very clear and the pages and bars are evenly spaced. Weber's autograph fair copy was clearly used as the main source, for the copyist not only retained, word for word, the movements' various specifications of instrumentation, the movement titles and tempo markings, but also kept with graphic precision to the layout of the source-text. Weber checked this copy very thoroughly and added innumerable details of dynamics, tempo, articulation and phrasing, while evidently – as indeed with other works – paying little attention to the correctness of the notes. Comparison of the two sources also shows that Weber apparently marked the copy without reference to his autograph, since different styles of marking can be found in certain places. As the copy-text directly intended for use in the preparation of the printed edition, this manuscript contains the work in its definitive form. Since it is doubtful whether Weber corrected the printer's proofs, and since the engraver reproduced some details of the manuscript imprecisely and misunderstood others, it is the engraver's copy-text, not the first edition, that constitutes the principal source for the present edition of the work.

3. Schlesinger's first edition
Berlin: Adolph Martin Schlesinger, plate number "253" (1817); no opus number on the title-page

In comparison with the engraver' copy, the first printed edition contains relatively few transmission errors, although some markings relating to dynamics and articulation have not been carried over. As in most of the Schlesinger editions of this period, Weber's vertical strokes indicating *staccato* have almost all been reproduced as dots. Alterations other than those resulting from misunderstandings and free interpretation are extremely few in number, as are additions of the engraver's own.

The publication history of the work and the Baermann edition

Like almost all of Weber's chamber works, the *Grand Duo* – which soon became part of the standard clarinet repertoire – has had a complicated publication history. One of the main lines of transmission is provided by the series of printed editions produced by Weber's main publisher Adolph Martin Schlesinger in Berlin, by Schlesinger's son Moritz in Paris and by Schlesinger's successor, the publisher Lienau. Of particular interest here is the link to the editions by Heinrich Baermann's son Carl Baermann, which were produced by the same publishing house. (These different lines of provenance are described in detail in Vol. VI/3 of WeGA, pp. 150-164 and analysed with reference to various particularly striking 'improvements' and errors).
In late 1869 Carl Baermann produced a new edition of the Grand Duo as part of his new edition of Weber's clarinet works for Schlesinger's *Gesammtausgabe*. Baermann carefully studied the piano part in the posthumous Schlesinger edition, removed outstanding errors and brought about some clarification of the musical text through his method of notation; he also supplied the solo part with detailed markings. While on this occasion he refrained from making alterations to the pitch or duration of notes, the edition is strewn with markings prescribing articulation, phrasing and dynamics. In particular, numerous accents and *crescendo-decrescendo* patterns, mainly one or two bars in length, have been added. In some cases *legato* slurs have been changed into *staccato* markings (for instance in the first movement, bar 47ff. or in the semiquaver figures in the clarinet part in the third movement, e.g. bars 13/14). Occasionally, too, *staccato* passages are interrupted by the addition of short slurs.

The effect created by the setting of accents against the strong beats, which Weber saved until the end of the third movement (bars 236ff.), is brought forward by Baermann to the first appearance of the *grazioso* idea (cf. bars 68ff.). At the start of the slow movement in bar 5 of the clarinet part the marking *"con duolo"* is replaced with *"con tutt'anima"* and in place of the *decrescendo* beginning at bar 63 Baermann initially marks a *crescendo*. The *"ritard."* in bar 141 of the first movement is also an addition. In the third movement Baermann attempts to give greater precision to the continuations of the clarinet trills in bars 196f. and 200f., which are not clear in Weber's notation, by adding a quaver grace note *b* before bars 197 and 201 respectively.

Despite these highly detailed specifications of articulation and dynamics, running counter to the musical text as handed down to us, the number of Baermann's interventions in the present instance is small in comparison with those in his editions of the other clarinet works. The Baermann edition was subsequently used as the basis for fresh arrangements and later editions of the work and thus had a direct or indirect influence on our whole experience of the *Grand Duo*. The present edition goes back to the "pre-Baermann" state of the work. Musicians familiar with the Baermann edition will notice that the original phrase marks extend further and that the articulation is more evenly indicated, so that the charge of being "short-winded", which has beset the work over the course of its history, can be set aside. We should emphasize that the definition of details in the printed score was particularly important to Weber – the finely detailed variants in articulation in the Rondo theme (bars 68ff. And 236ff.) are evidence of this.

The present edition and some of the idiosyncrasies of Weber's notation

As far as possible, the notation of the new edition adheres to that of the principal sources, in keeping with the principles of the WeGA. Additions corroborated by other source documents appear in round brackets, with details added by the editor in square brackets. It should be borne in mind that passages that are unmarked should seldom be taken literally, i.e. the absence of markings does not automatically mean that preceding indications of articulation have ceased to apply. Rather, bars of this kind may need to be interpreted either in the light of parallel passages or in line with Weber's frequent practice of using variants. For example, in the first movement it seems obvious that the *staccati* should be carried over to the r.h. in bars 139 and 161 to match the preceding parallel passage.

By and large, the shorthand devices indicating repetitions of notes and chords which are often used both by Weber and by the copyists of the engraver's copy-texts have been retained; they have been written out in full, however, in cases where their retention would have created unnecessary confusion for the performer. The rhythmic values of grace notes and terminations accompanying single notes and trills vary both between sources and often within a single manuscript. In the case of grace notes Weber tends to use the form ♪ for single notes and demisemiquavers in the case of two or more notes, regardless of the metre. For **appoggiaturas** Weber sometimes uses ♪ and sometimes normal, smaller-size quavers. The copyist usually adopted the form of grace notes used by Weber.

The distinctive features of Weber's slurring have been retained, but in places they make for unwieldiness in the score and pose a challenge to the performer. Weber's imprecise and inconsistent use of slurs makes it impossible to tell in the *Rondo* theme in the third movement to what extent the many discrepancies are intentional and whether some of them are the result of carelessness in notation or whether they indicate a distinction between **phrasing and articulation** marks. Even where the bass figure is taken up in the middle section in bars 136ff. it is difficult to tell whether a differentiation is intended. The editor has therefore reproduced the slurs with the precision found in the source document and just introduced a few careful corrections (marked as such). To indicate *sempre legato* or *sempre portato* playing in repeated or continuous accompaniment figures, Weber consistently uses phrasal slurs extending over several bars: at times these alternate arbitrarily with single- or multiple-bar (and often also overlapping or contiguous) slurs. In such cases the slurs should not be misread as indicating the start of a new section for articulation. This point is borne out by the variations in the notation of the various sources observable here (see for example the piano writing in bars 64ff., 88ff., 126ff. and 259ff in the first movement, bars 9ff. and 71ff. in the second movement and bars 163ff. in the third movement). Further problems arise with Alberti-style accompaniment figures (e.g. first movement, bar 259ff.), where the contiguous slurs of variable length in the r.h. merely indicate *legato* playing, while the imprecisely placed slurs at the beginning of the second movement, bars 5 and 8ff. merely indicate a *portato*. The use of slurs spanning rests and of open-ended slurs in repeated figures (such as those in the third movement, bars 61–62, r.h. or bars 147–150, lower system) demonstrate particularly clearly that these slurs merely indicate a way of playing and are not structural markers.

The precise significance of the distinction between dots and vertical strokes in Weber remains unresolved, but the distinction is again found in the *Grand Duo* and – to the extent that it can be clearly established – is retained in this edition. The copyist of the engraver's copy-text used dots throughout; the added vertical strokes are later entries of Weber's, most of which were then amended to dots before printing. Weber's use of a vertical stroke at the end of a slur is also a distinctive feature of his notation. It seems clear that the purpose is to indicate a shortening of the note value. The same is true of the vertical strokes at the beginning or in the middle of the slur, for example in the first movement, bars 253–254, l.h.

Within Weber's indications of **dynamics**, which leave many gaps and are often difficult to guess, his markings of **accents** are sometimes difficult to interpret too, as their size makes them scarcely distinguishable from decrescendo hairpins. Even immediately successive, motivically identical passages may be marked differently, as for instance in the clarinet part in the third movement (see the length of a decrescendo hairpin in bar 212 of the engraver's copy and a normal accent sign in bar 214; both are additions by Weber). In such instances the editors have been obliged to reproduce their respective readings in the Edited Text.

A characteristic example of this problem is a correction made by Weber in the third movement, where in bar 17 the copyist had retained the accent on the long note in the clarinet, but Weber then wrote *fp* over it: it would seem that the two forms of marking are not synonymous for Weber. Although – as the entry in the autograph score shows – he presumably preferred the 'simpler' form of notation because it was easier to write, it seems the accent sign can essentially be interpreted in two ways. In other words, the possibility of differentiation must always be borne in mind, especially with long note values. (Another indication of the distinctions involved is provided by an alteration in bar 59, where in the clarinet part Weber overwrites the accent, which the copyist had again carried over from the autograph score, with a fairly long decrescendo hairpin extending the whole duration of the note. At the same time, however, he replaces the accent in the l.h. with an *fp*).

Weber's **notation for the piano** differs from modern convention inasmuch as he often uses the staves in order to make clear the musical flow or the part-writing. His common practices of notating the two hands on one stave (e.g. first movement, bars 126ff.), and of continuing a figure on a different stave from the one in which it has begun (e.g. first movement, bars 166ff. and 198ff.), both exemplify this desire to make clear the sequence of musical events and have been retained in the present edition.

Weber supplied pedal markings only at the *portati* in bars 37ff. and 51 in the second movement, and in bar 217 in the third movement. In the latter two cases, raising the dampers serves to reinforce the G major chordal sonority and the repetitions of the B flat major seventh chord respectively, and in the first case the aim is clearly to bring out the sonority of the high register in the r.h. in a similar way. (Weber's Brodmann grand piano had, in addition to the damper pedal, an *una corda* pedal, a bassoon stop and a *piano* pedal; in this instance, however, only the raising of the dampers seems to be indicated.) Pedal changes here are presumably also indicated by the slurring.

There are different ways of interpreting the shorthand notation of the demisemiquaver **tremoli** in the finale, bars 125ff., as indeed the various editions of the work show.

Alternative notes are given for the clarinet in the first half of bar 196 in the first movement, perhaps to take account of the instrument's technical features. Obviously the difficulties do not result from individual notes but from playing the first three notes in sequence. The notation of the clarinet part at the beginning of the development section of the first movement (bars 130bff.) has been retained for the sake of legibility, although the marking style is actually incorrect.

Heartfelt thanks go at this point to all those who have contributed to the preparation of this edition.

Knut Holtsträter
Translation Julia Rushworth

Grand Duo concertant

Carl Maria von Weber
1786–1826
(WeV P. 12)

*) In den Quellen keine Bezeichnung der Dynamik.

© 2005 Schott Music GmbH & Co. KG, Mainz

*) Bogenkorrektur vom Hg. übernommen nach Webers Autograph (vgl. auch T. 284).

*) In den Quellen keine Bezeichnung der Dynamik.

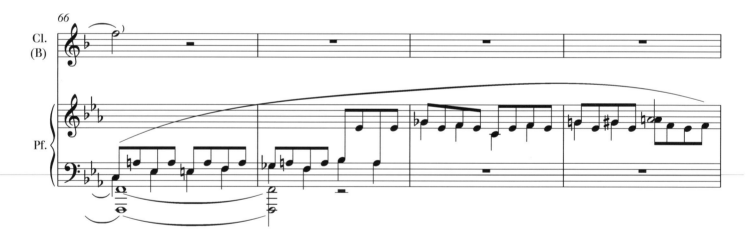

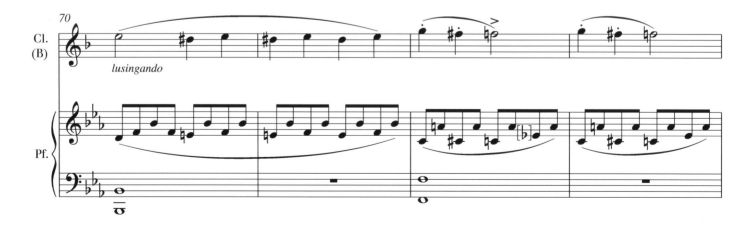

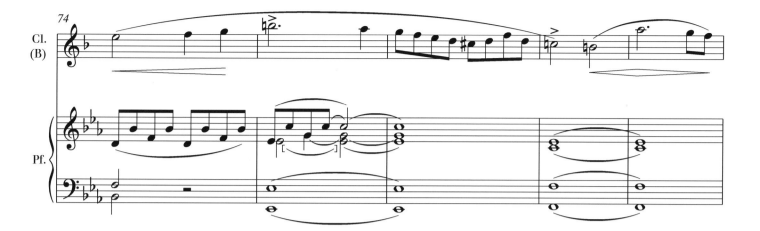

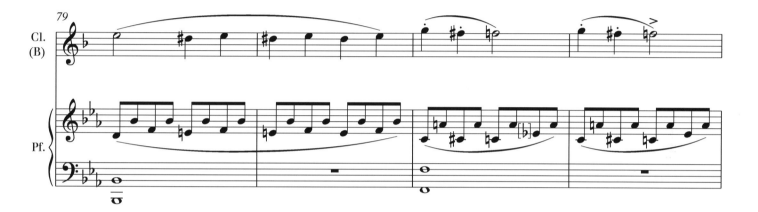

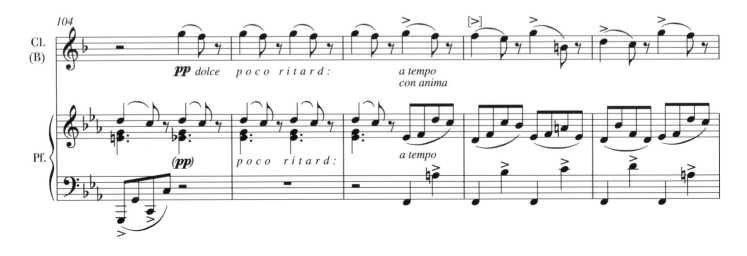

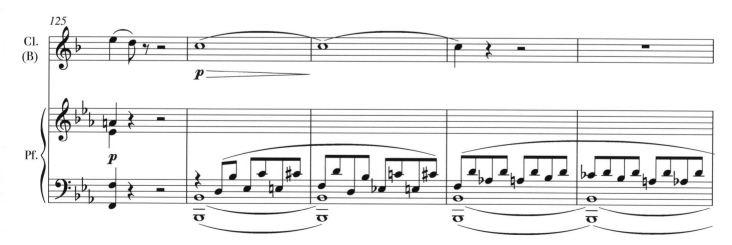

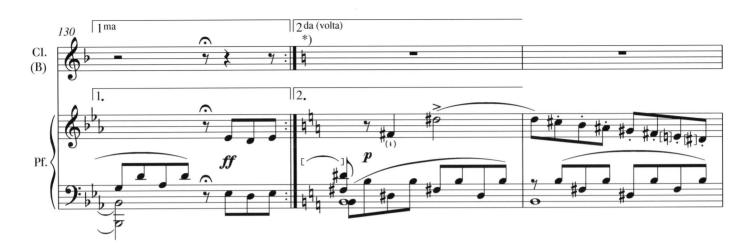

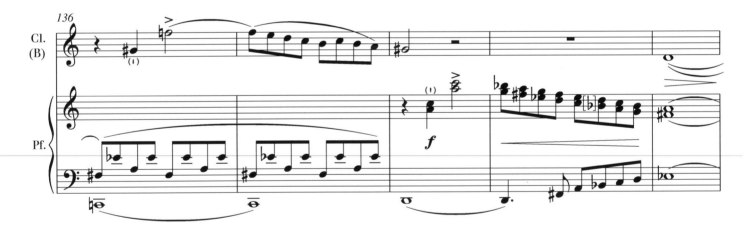

*) Die (inkonsequente) Bezeichnung des Tonartwechsels ist vom Hg. unverändert übernommen.

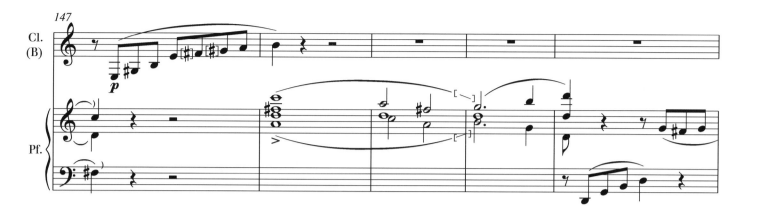

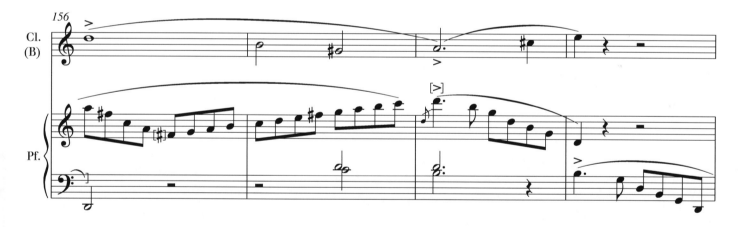

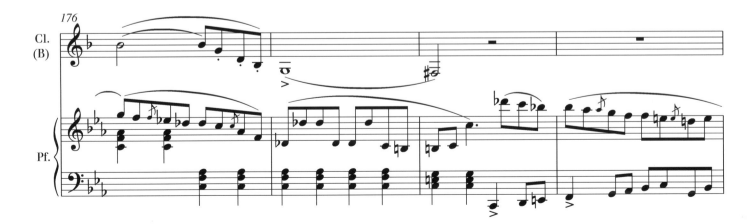

*) Artikulation der rH vom Hg. korrigiert in Analogie zu T. 168ff.

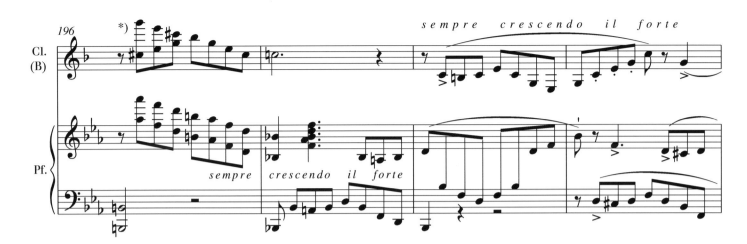

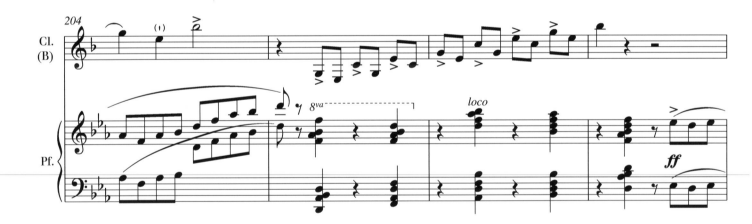

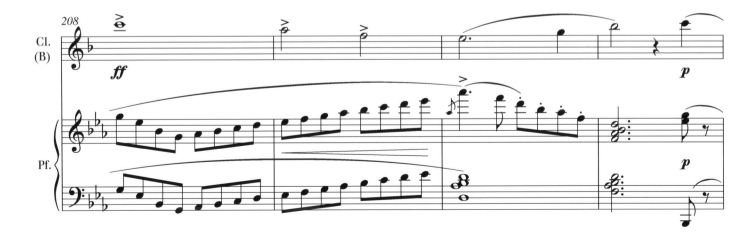

*) Zur Variante der Klarinette vgl. Vorwort.

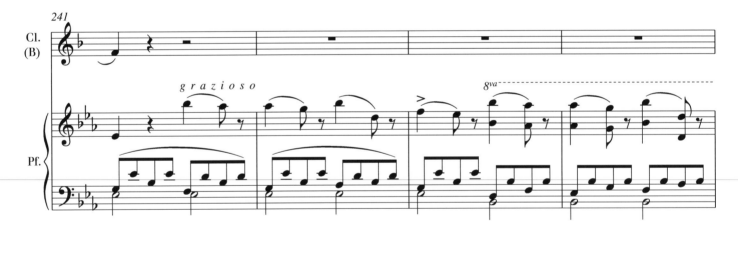

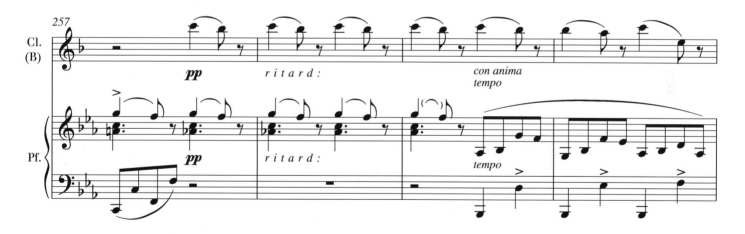

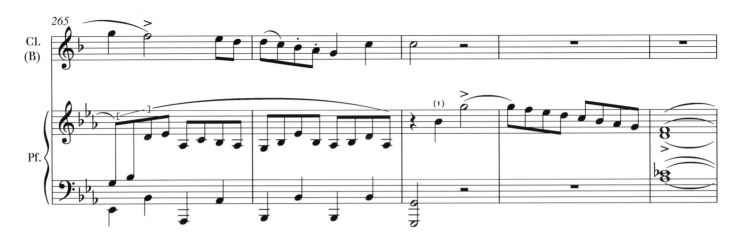

Edition Schott

Clarinet Library · Klarinetten-Bibliothek

Carl Maria von Weber

1786 – 1826

Grand Duo concertant

for Clarinet (in B♭) and Piano
für Klarinette (in B) und Klavier

opus 48 (JV 204, WeV P. 12)

Nach dem Text der Carl-Maria-von Weber-Gesamtausgabe herausgegeben von
Edited from Carl Maria von Weber, Complete Works by
Knut Holtsträter

KLB 58
ISMN 979-0-001-14095-9

Clarinetto in B♭

www.schott-music.com

SCHOTT

Mainz · London · Berlin · Madrid · New York · Paris · Prag · Tokyo · Toronto
© 2005 SCHOTT MUSIC GmbH & Co. KG, Mainz · Printed in Germany

Grand Duo concertant

Carl Maria von Weber
1786–1826
(WeV P. 12)

61

ffz   perdendosi

70

[p] lusingando

76

81

86

tr   3

94

1   f   5

104

pp dolce   poco ritard: a tempo
con anima

109

114

5   f

124

p   p

1ᵐᵃ   2 da volta
1   2

4

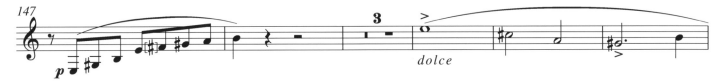

*) Zur Variante der Kl. vgl. Vorwort.

4

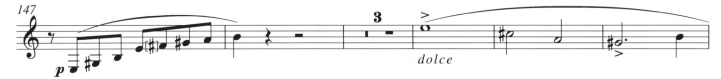

*) Zur Variante der Kl. vgl. Vorwort.

sempre crescendo il forte

6

257

pp   *ritard:*   *con anima*
                              tempo

262

267

f

278

p

283

287

291

tr   *f*   *ff*

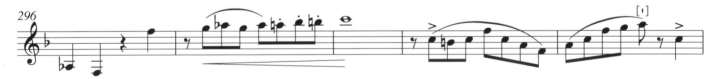

296

301

ff

305

Andante con moto

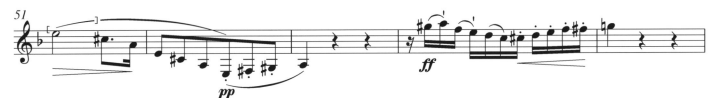

*) In den Quellen keine Angabe zur Dynamik.

Rondo. Allegro

con grazia

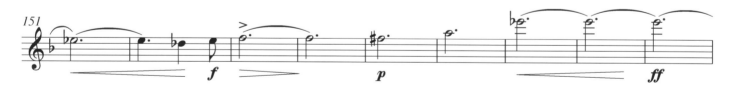

*) Zu der wiederum uneinheitlichen Artikulationsbezeichnung vgl. Vorwort.

12

26

Andante con moto

*) Zur Instrumentenbezeichnung vgl. Vorwort.

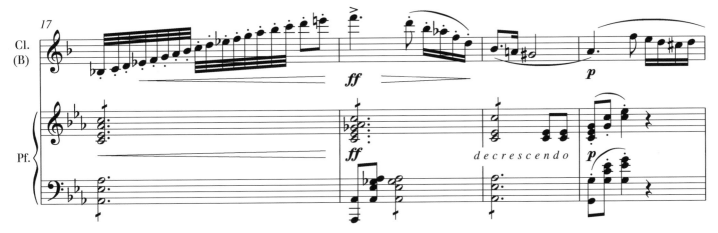

*) Die eigentümlich gemischte Artikulations-/Phrasierungsbezeichnung der T. 24–26 folgt der Hauptquelle.

*) Im Autograph eine Variante der T. 32³–33¹, die zunächst in die Stichvorlage übernommen, von Weber aber in die vorliegende Form geändert wurde.

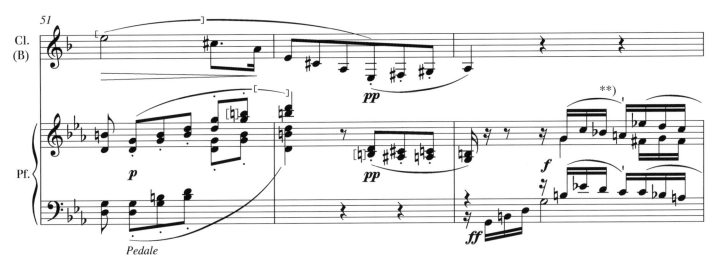

*) Variante im Autograph (rH wie T. 42).
**) Im Autograph Auflöser vor h¹; vgl. dazu KB der WeGA.

Rondo. Allegro

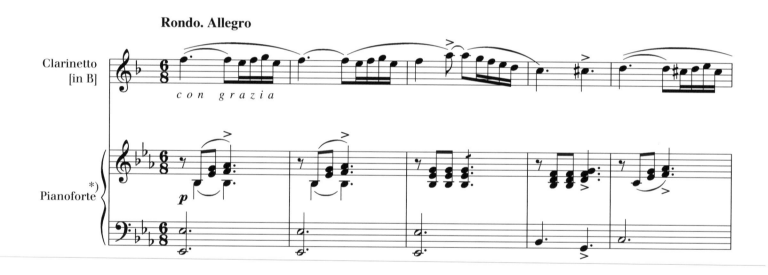

*) Zur Instrumentenbezeichnung vgl. Vorwort.

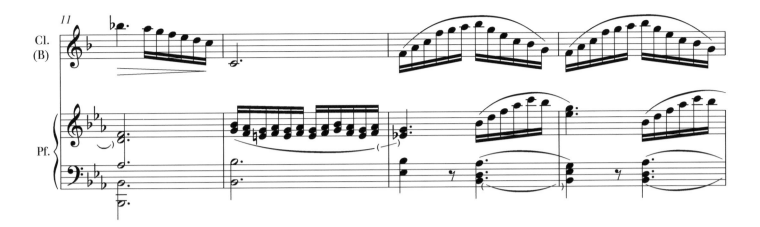

*) Zu Webers Korrektur vgl. Vorwort.

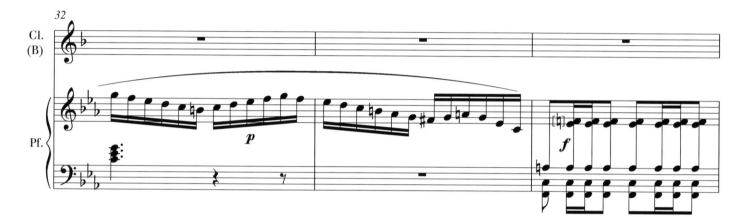

*) Zur uneinheitlich bezeichneten Artikulation vgl. Vorwort.

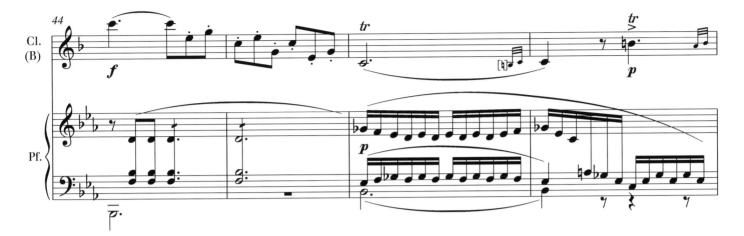

*) Zu Webers Korrekturen vgl. Vorwort.

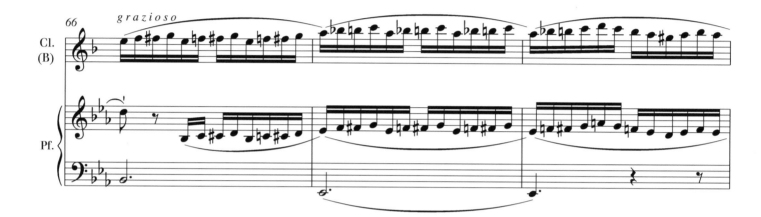

*) Zur Artikulation und Phrasierung der lH T. 73–80 vgl. KB der WeGA, S. 269.

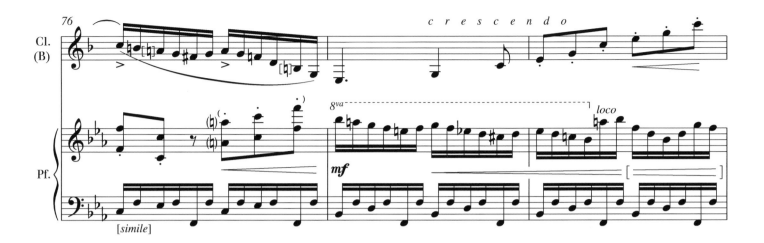

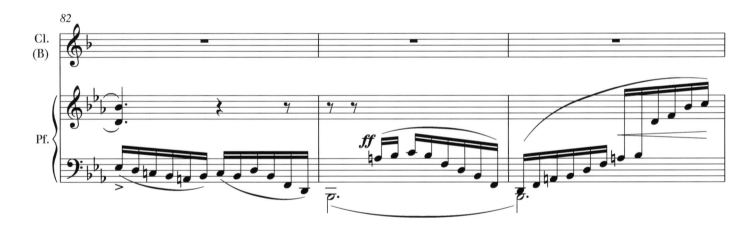

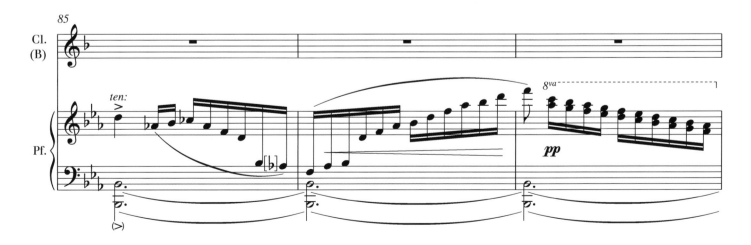

38

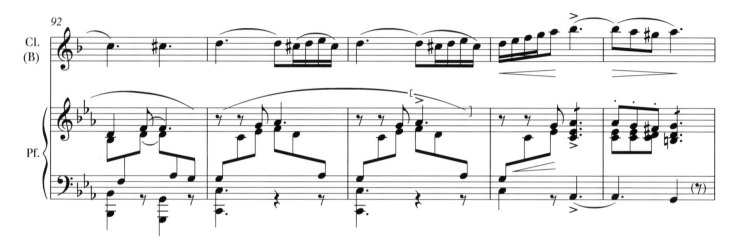

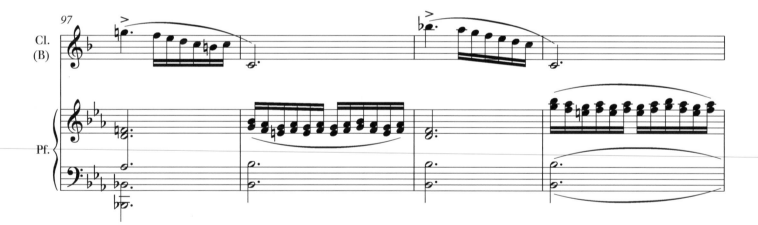

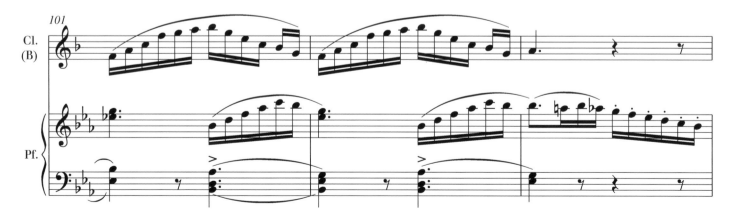

*) Zur wiederum uneinheitlich bezeichneten Artikulation vgl. Vorwort.

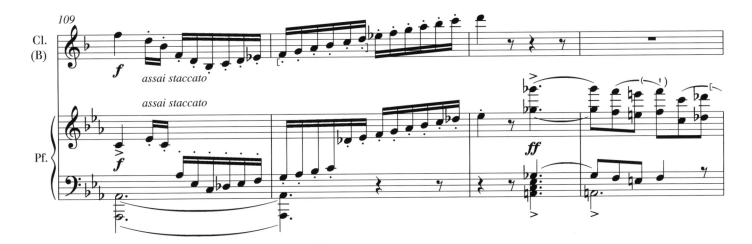

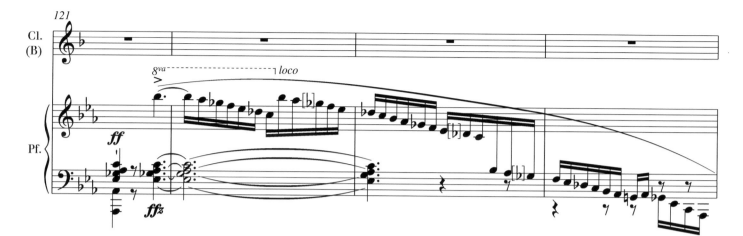

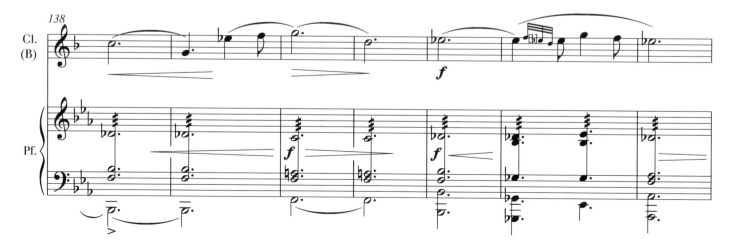

*) In der lH trotz Akzent Haltebogen von T. 167–168; vom Hg. angeglichen an T. 172f.

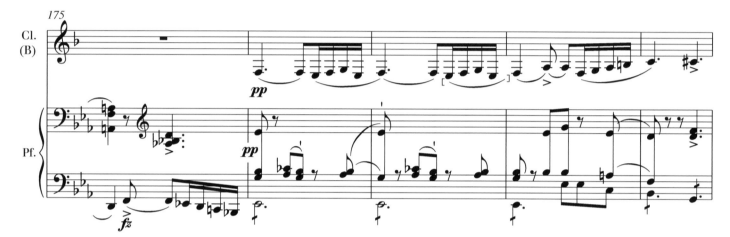

44

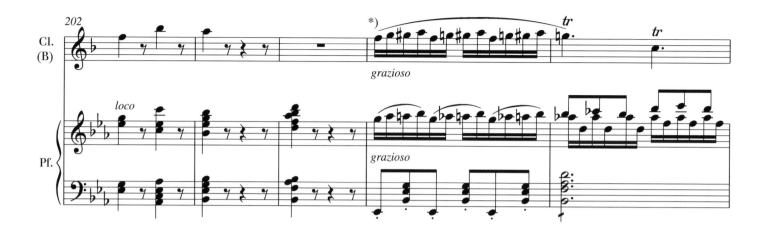

*) Nebeneinander von Phrasierungs- und Artikulationsbögen vom Hg. unverändert übernommen.

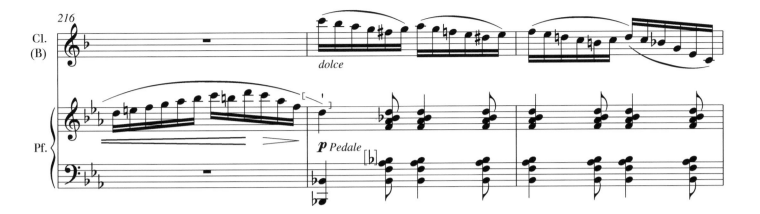

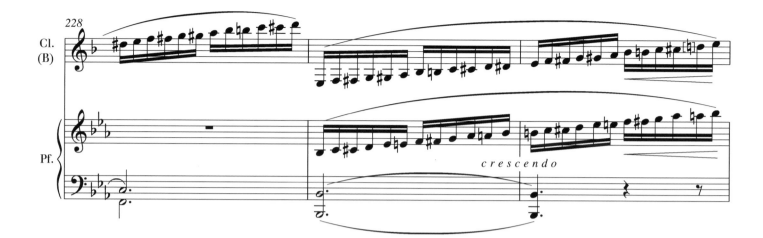

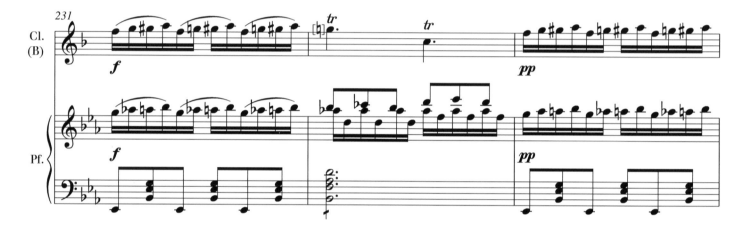

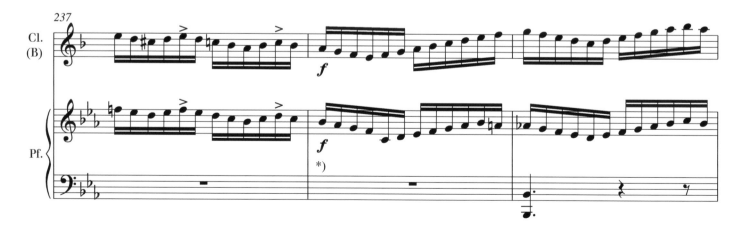

*) Im Autograph nachträglich eingefügt:

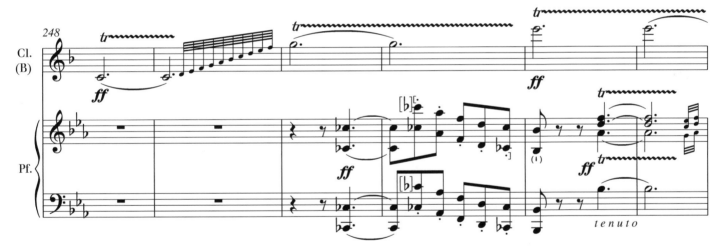

*) Im Autograph *dolce* statt **pp**.

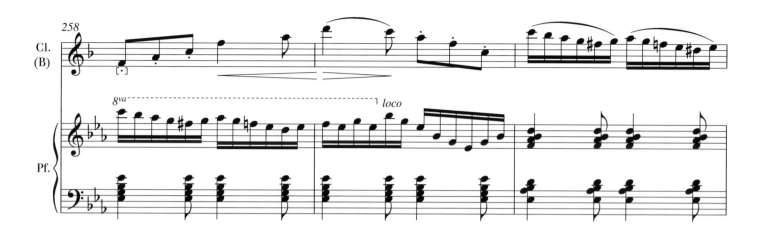

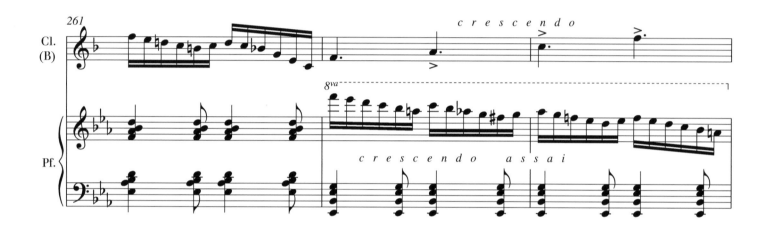

Schott Music, Mainz 52 026